CW00642548

# It's a
# Newton

# It's a Newton

# Newton

Charles Buchan Ritchie

First published by CBR Books in 2008.

Head office Glenugie Engineering Works, Peterhead,
Aberdeenshire, AB42 0YX.

Printed in the UK.

ISBN 978-0-9560843-0-9

A catalogue record for this book is available from the
British Library.

Additional copies can be purchased by contacting
newton@score-group.com

*Beryl is my inspiration*

Some part of what follows has been inspired by the thoughts of other individuals too numerous to mention. I of course acknowledge this and thank them for planting these seeds in my mind. If I have offended any parties it was not my intent and if you bring it to my attention I will ensure the necessary changes are made to the text.

Thank you to the team that helped me create this book, namely Anita Voll (text), Chantelle Proctor (text), Benjamin Mooney (visuals), and David Anderson (visuals).

**Charles Buchan Ritchie**
June 2008

# Contents

CHAPTER 1

# About the Author

I am going to write this book on engineering without using one formula.

I am Charles Buchan Ritchie. I was born on 22nd October 1947 at a place called St Combs, Aberdeenshire, Scotland. My forefathers lived in the areas of St Combs, Inverallochy and Cairnbulg which are all part of the Buchan area of Aberdeenshire. These people were a mixture of fishing and agricultural stock. I am the first person in my family to work in the engineering industry.

I was educated in St Combs Primary School then at Fraserburgh Academy, which I left at the age of 15 with no formal qualifications.

I then subsequently served a 5 year apprenticeship at the Consolidated Pneumatic Tool Company in Fraserburgh, Scotland as a fitter turner. This is where I learned the practical aspects of my trade.

The theoretical aspect of my trade I gained through night school at Banff and Buchan College of Further Education, Fraserburgh in Scotland and at Robert Gordon's Institute in Aberdeen, Scotland.

When I was 22 I gained a Higher National Certificate in Engineering, my hot subject being thermodynamic studies.

I married my wife when I was 20 and we had 3 sons by the time I was 30.

After my apprenticeship I then went to the University of Strathclyde in Glasgow, Scotland for 2 years and received a BSC Degree in Mechanical Engineering. My thesis was on sound.

My wife, who was working as a primary school teacher, paid for my university fees and supported me while at university.

Following on from University I worked as a Manufacturing Engineering Manager in Cleveland Twist Drill Company in Peterhead, Scotland.

At this time I took a diploma in Management at Robert Gordon's Institute in Aberdeen. This is where I picked up a little knowledge of accounts, law, human behaviour, and computing. The thesis was on a model factory in the mainframe of a computer.

After this I joined the offshore oil industry based in the North Sea working with an Aberdeen contracting company.

In 1982 I departed that company and formed what is now the Score Group of Companies whose head office is located in Peterhead, Scotland. The company is currently active in 36 different locations throughout the world in engineering support for the oil and gas, utility, chemically, pharmaceutical and defence industry globally.

My principal interest has always been giving people who have an interest in engineering similar opportunities and experiences to those which have shaped me. I regularly lecture to the company's apprenticeship groups which number 250 team members and the contents of what follows form part of these lectures.

I have written this book to share my thoughts, knowledge and practical experiences given to me by many mentors throughout my life, all of whom I thank for enabling me to see this world from different perspectives. That said, this is my current personal view of these subjects. If you the reader can suggest other views I would be obliged and you can contact me by e-mail on **newton@score-group.com**.

**CHAPTER 2**

# Newton and Force

All through my life and up to fairly recently I have had a problem coming to terms with a newton. I did not fully understand what it was.

The 'newton' conceived by Sir Isaac became the basic unit of measurement for force.

My problem and that of many others was that I had to choose other words, like mass and acceleration, etc. to aid me in trying to find the secret of the newton.

This confused me as I had no proper understanding of mass and acceleration, etc. Therefore, I could not emerge from the confusion. I was lost.

Bearing in mind, over the 45 years I'd been working with newtons, I played with newtons successfully both mathematically and practically, but something troubled me – being able to find the solution without really knowing the building blocks. As in most things I was looking for the corner stone without which all understanding falls away like a house of cards.

I will continue searching today and will be searching tomorrow.

I saved my sanity and my humour by recalling the words of a professor in Strathclyde University when he saw that I was struggling with a concept called 'entropy.' We find this word reoccurring in the theory of thermodynamics where the theory of entropy was developed by William John Macquorn Rankine (Lord Rankine, born 5 July 1820 in Edinburgh, Scotland; died 24 December 1872 in Glasgow, Scotland). In my opinion the greatest Scottish engineer who ever lived.

Entropy is the measure of disorder within a thermodynamic system whose value greatly depends on the temperature of the system. At absolute zero degrees entropy is presumed to be zero.

Here I was working with the formulas finding the answer but clearly not appreciating the question. What I needed was a better definition that would stop me going around in circles (if this book is well received I am going to do another one on heat, temperature and entropy). The professor said to me 'Charles, anything that can be defined is not worth defining.' Here then is the newton – that which defies definition. It may equal something but what it is, it is. The corner stone of the entire known universe – indefinable.

I should also mention here another famous Scot who laid the foundation of modern physics in such fields as special relativity and Quantum mechanics. James Clerk Maxwell (born 2 June 1831 in Edinburgh, Scotland; died 5 November 1879 in Cambridge, England).

I now realised that I must find another way to appreciate what a newton is.

I then went back to the middle of the 17th century in England and imagined I was sitting next to Sir Isaac Newton (born on 4 January 1643 in Woolsthrope, Lincolnshire, England; died 31 March 1727 in Kensington, London, England)

Newton and Force

when an apple from an apple tree fell on his head and he replied "I have been struck by a force, I am going to call it 'a newton'". Isaac, being a mathematician, immediately thereafter produced a whole set of formulas that for the next 300 years established how we, the engineering world, would view the local universe.

The formulas produced by newton confused people like me and whilst we used them to resolve issues, the equations became ever more obscure rather than clarifying the nature of reality.

I was therefore determined not to use any formulas when talking to the engineering apprentices and trainees, endeavouring to give them an intuitive understanding of the basic building blocks of engineering, I went back to meet Sir Isaac sitting under the tree and came to the conclusion that the human sense of feel was what Sir Isaac felt happened to him under that tree.
He was touched by the falling apple and concluded that that touch was the

equivalent to the concept of one newton of force.

When I came to this conclusion I, like Archimedes (born 287 BC in Syracuse, Sicily; died in 212 BC Syracuse, Sicily) in the bath, shouted 'Eureka'.

I, then, and in every lecture thereafter start with the concept of a newton. The means of conveying this message is that I take up my fist and punch the person nearest to me on the shoulder with that force, I then determine that to be my one newton of force. I then ask all members in the room to strike one another in a similar fashion. By this experience they now all have the feeling of what Sir Isaac experienced under the apple tree.

With this feeling in our mind we can now build the future intuitively but before we depart from the newton, let us consider where it has come from and other peculiarities of this thing we now know exists by feel.

Where does it come from?

The process and sequence of events

Newton and Force

that makes the newton real is as follows.

The force that you have created in punching your friend's shoulder has come from within your own body. Your body has derived the ability to generate this force by virtue of the food it has eaten. This food owes its existence to the sun in the heavens. The sun itself is powered by thermo-nuclear fusion reactions. The sun exists as part of a galaxy and we are led to believe that this galaxy was formed by a concept called the 'big bang'. Prior to the big bang there are those of us who believe something called 'God willed it'. God had one hand in the big bang at least.

So we now know where the newton came from, it came from the big bang.

The other feature of the newton we know about is it always wants to travel in a straight line. However, this direction of travel can be bent if it is subjected to other forces, e.g. gravitational or electromagnetical forces. In figure 1 below I have shown the idealistic movement of newtons within the big bang's sphere.

So there we have the pathway of the newton felt when someone hits you on your shoulder.

Where does it go to?

My current thinking on this using the concept that all actions have equal and opposite reactions is that a newton that comes from the big bang must go back to the big bang. I have often found this difficult to comprehend as I cannot see the roads these newtons are travelling on nor speed of travel and, (as I am told that the speed cannot be faster than that of the speed of light, according to Albert Einstein (born 14 March 1879 in Ulm Germany, died 18 April 1955 in Princeton, New Jersey, USA), he of theory of relativity fame) when one considers the infinite time and the infinite newtons that are out there, I have a problem.

I have addressed this problem by asking the question in my lectures 'where does the newton come from and where does it go?' The best answer I have ever been given came from a 16 year old apprentice in 2004. His answer was

'Charles, I do not know where it comes from, I only know it was here for a time and went away.' His surname was not Einstein (if the reader can give me a better answer I would like to hear it . . . ).

Similarly, newtons exist, massive amounts of them. They are connections to God. To find out more we must go beyond the horizon of the big bang into nothingness to find the breeding ground or are they bred inside the big bang sphere? My view is the former.

The big bang horizon consumes something, the products of which are newtons and its big buddy time, see figure 1.

It's a Newton

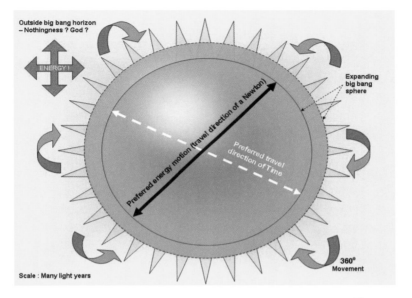

Outside big bang horizon
– Nothingness ? God ?

ENERGY !

Expanding
big bang
sphere

Preferred energy motion (travel direction of a Newton)

Preferred travel direction of Time

360°
Movement

Scale : Many light years

*Figure 1*

## CHAPTER 3

# Time and Space

Time is another concept that I have had great problems coming to terms with throughout my life. I now observe time through my eyes.

I see it and the means by which I see it is I observe motion. I look at the leaves and trees moving in the wind and I see time, I look at the views of the sea and I see time. We also can hear wind on the leaves and the breaking of the waves on the shore. By this means we also sense motion.

Time has a great and close affinity to a newton now in my mind. If they're not the same thing they're joined together like Siamese twins. They have some common shared properties.

In the previous chapter we came to the conclusion that the newton originated from the big bang. If you follow the motion of time both past and present you will come to the conclusion that time 'motion' also comes from the big bang and is going back to the big bang.

We also noted that newtons prefer to travel in a straight line and may only be altered from that straight line motion if subjected to external forces, i.e. gravitational or electromagnetical, etc. The size of these external forces affect the direction of the newton away from a straight line. These external forces bend the straight line.

It is therefore safe to presume that a similar effect happens with the direction of time, i.e. the straight line of time will also bend like the newtons' direction subject to external forces.

We will now take a look at Space.

Space is a volumetric concept. My thinking is that space is the volume between two time frames. Space will be that volume uncompressed between the motion of one second from one to two seconds. If the space is measured in light years the distance between one and two light years will be that volume of space entrapped within that distance. By this means we can envisage space.

A common property shared by time, newtons and space is in zero time – there will be zero newtons, zero space. Similarly in zero newtons there will be zero time and zero space. These concepts are all linked within the big bang sphere and of course their motions may all bend.

Some day I will write on my vision of that area beyond the expanding horizon at the leading edge of the big bang; that is the area outwith the outer skin of the big bang. The horizon of which according to most observers is currently receding.

In the interim I will go back to time and of course there are many ways humans have tried to conceptualise this thing. Some groups believe that time motion flows over you and you are powerless to affect any changes in this regular flow. That what happens to you is in some ways preordained.

I went through a period of time where I thought this also until I was sitting on a beach and enjoying a black rum in the Caribbean island of Tobago. I was reading a poem written by a native of the island and the essence of this poem is 'you may sit and watch time flow through you and blame others for your misfortune or you may get up, be active and walk into time, eventually finding a different place to observe the motion of time'. I now believe this to be a better model. Time is what you make of it.

This summer in 2008 I am in Stavanger, Norway living in a boat in the harbour. I find this place conducive to thought and sitting watching the waves in the Fjord I got to thinking about the bend in newtons, time and space and I came to the conclusion that this bend must be capable of going through at least one circumference of 360 degrees.

A very interesting concept indeed but how else can it start from the big bang and go back to the same place it started? This means that there is a place somewhere where we can go back in time to the beginning of motion or any place in between.

You may be wondering what this has to do with engineering. Engineering is the

It's a Newton

application of ingenuity to practical problems and as there is nothing new under the sun or within the sphere of the big bang, the newton, time and space, using these explanations, are far easier to comprehend and to play with. From the above we can deduce there is no such thing as empty space.

CHAPTER 4

# Time and Matter

In the previous chapters we concluded that both the passage of the newton and time is travelling through a place called space from and to the boundary horizon of the big bang, and the preferred direction taken by these objects is a straight line.

However, we also know that the probability is that the directions all bend, twist and turn along the way, going and coming. We must ask ourselves; do any of them stop along the way? Is there a hotel or resting house they book in to and out of and we find there is – why?

It's because we see and feel these resting places. What is this place? It is the place where there is a lump of matter which has a mass. It could be a carrot that we eat, a skyscraper, the planet Saturn or any other piece of matter. The newtons, the time and the space they take up are stored here in this battery appearing to be at rest and this may be their preferred state. That of inertia or otherwise running around inside an uncompressed space by this volume created by the big bang. Perhaps this location called matter is the home of their choice part time between their motions back and forward to the boundary of the big bang.

However, we again have a problem here and once again we've to address this problem by consulting with another very famous engineer whose name was William Thomson, better known as Lord Kelvin (born 26 June 1824 in Belfast; died 17 December 1907, Netherhall (near Largs), Ayrshire, Scotland). He, of absolute zero temperature fame, a condition like absolute vacuum that is impossible to obtain because of the boundary issue. Physical boundaries always leak, therefore, for example, perfect vacuums can never be realised in practice as particles will migrate from the boundary wall into the vacuum mitigating its perfection. Further of course, if we examine subatomically all

It's a Newton

these masses apparently at rest, a whole state of continuing motion is going on in the subatomic particles, such as the electron, etc.

So here we have it, we have newtons, we have time, we have matter and we have space all within the big bang. Thanks be to God.

What is beyond the big bang?

My conclusion is a whole bunch of matter (mass). The form this mass takes may be different from the mass transformed that goes through the boundary of the big bang horizon. We should hope there is plenty of it, for if there is not we are all going to implode (dream on).

Could this matter be positive because we can see and feel it? Is there a negative component that we can neither feel nor see? The concept of a black hole springs to mind here although we can see them and for sure if you're in the near vicinity, you're going to feel them. However, I will leave that to the physicists.

So now we have time which we detect by seeing motion – zero time zero motion.

When we consider positive time, we see the emergence of such concepts as length, distance, speed, acceleration, etc. and again none of these concepts we see in zero time as they derive their existence from positive time.

Negative time must exist somewhere if only in this sentence. I will leave that for another book.

So now we have space. That volume encompassed between two time periods. We also know that this volume of space is far from empty. It's got, within it many newtons, time, some mass as a result, flowing through it and it exists because we observe it.

The position from which we observe it brings us, of course, to Albert Einstein's theories.

I have redone figure 1 of the sphere of the big bang superimposing the newtons' travel and time travel through the space, little chunks which we can imagine to be matter or mass (see figure 2). All of these, depending on their size affect the near motion of newtons, time and space, distorting the travel of same and stopping completely in some instances.

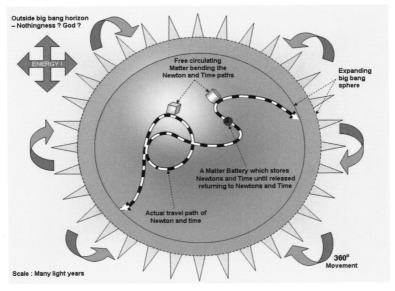

*Figure 2*

Time and Matter

## CHAPTER 5

# Energy, Newton and Time

How do I try to convey the concept of energy to the apprentices? I start always with what is a newton. I ask them as I highlighted in chapter one to punch one another with a force of one newton. Then, after we establish the force, we look to the motion of the force. We then come to the conclusion that energy is a newton in time.

A newton is attached by some means to a period of time to make energy. Large energies are either a small amount of newtons attached to a large time or a large amount of newtons attached to a small time. If we can conceive a position of no newtons and some time there will be no energy. If we can conceive a position of no time and some newtons there will be no energy.

Similarly, we can comment that the

NOTES

search for all energy begins at the big bang horizon and goes back to the big bang horizon. That energy travels like its component parts in a straight line but like its component parts can be bent.

A very handy thing God has given us – this big bang. The sphere within which the contents behave in a rational manner.

The method which I try to show newtons and time becoming energy is by utilising a standard work top bench, two pieces of wood, 100 millimetres by 75 millimetres and 75 millimetres thick, an elastic band and another piece of wood representing a wall – photo series of time based in figures 3, 4 and 5.

In figure 3 you will see a human fist imparting a force of one newton on one of the small pieces of wood. You will see that the piece of wood accelerates under that force until it meets the wall and stops. The photos give you the time elapsed between frames. You will note that at the end of the test sequence the piece of wood becomes stationary and the newton therefore has

Fig 3 – Travel and Time

Fig 4 – Travel Time and Impact

Fig 5 – Travel Time and Impact (Safe passenger)

disappeared somewhere. Time has elapsed also.

Figure 4 shows the identical process, the only differences being the two pieces of wood are now one on top of the other and then activated by a punch from a fist imparting again one newton. When this assembly meets the wall, the top piece separates from the bottom piece, they both come to rest and the newton disappears after the elapsed time again (as per figure 3).

If we study figure 4, at the instant after the point of impact we make an

Energy, Newton and Time

interesting observation – the newton has divided itself; one part of this division going into the car and subsequently disappearing when the car is at rest, the other part is still energising the passenger until it also disappears when the passenger comes to rest. We may deduce that a newton and packs of newtons are infinitely divisible and only exist within time.

In figure 5 the two pieces are held together by an elastic band and subjected to a force like before of one newton. This time when the assembly meets the wall, the top one attempts to leave the bottom one but is restrained by the elastic band. At the end of this process the newton again has disappeared as time has elapsed.

We now know where it has gone and where it came from in the first place.

I recommend you carry out this practical experiment. I have other methods of showing this transformation but this is currently my preferred method.
The reasons are many, not the least of them being the fact that the group of

apprentices that I lecture to are 20 times more prone to accidents away from their work place than in their work place. The most common accident after cut fingers are accidents involving motorcars, motorbikes and bicycles. Of course our company wants to have zero accidents.

These 3 sets of figures show the worktop as the road, the first small piece of wood is the car, the second piece is the passenger, the elastic band is the seatbelt and the longer part is the wall. I will describe a motorcar, passenger, newton, time and space where the energy goes and how it is dissipated. I will then highlight where a seatbelt may save lives on low energy collisions and where a seatbelt may not be able to save lives where even a small amount of newtons exist in small time or where large amounts of newtons exist in a large time.

Now that we have seen what has happened to the wood and the elastic band let us consider and visualise in our mind the motorcar, passenger and seatbelt.

Energy, Newton and Time

The motorcar derives its newtons from the fuel consumed within the engine. These newtons flow through the motorcar and the passenger and any other mass attached to the car giving the car motion. Once we see this motion, time has started. The newtons join with this time and energy is the result.

In the normal car, additional newtons are added over time producing acceleration and replacing those being lost due to friction, etc.

We go back to our experiment (figure 3) and we study the car now at rest following the collision with the wall. The car after this collision is at rest, in effect the car sees zero time and of course all the newtons have disappeared – gone back to the big bang.

When we now look at figure 4 at the point of impact, the passenger is not restrained by the seatbelt, has gone through the window of the car and is still travelling. The car is in the same condition as figure 3 – zero time zero newtons. The passenger however flying

It's a Newton

through the window has newton in motion therefore sees time. When the passenger comes to rest we are in a position of zero time and zero newtons in the passenger. The newtons have disappeared from the passenger and gone back to the big bang.

If we now look at figure 5, at the point of impact the passenger does not go through the window as the passenger is restrained by the seatbelt. Therefore the newtons that energise the passenger's motion following the impact in figure 4 must have transferred through the seatbelt to the car body. Therefore, after both passenger and the car come to rest, (i.e. zero time and zero newton) – newtons are away back to the big bang.

The reader on reading this will come to a conclusion that this is so obvious it makes sense. Why then are there so many accidents?

As an engineer I want to study how the newtons travel at the point of impact through the body.

As detailed in the last chapter, we now

understand that these newtons want to travel in a straight line and will do so until either bent or restrained by an equal force.

I then use this example to demonstrate how in some car accidents, people are killed wearing seatbelts with no apparent damage to the outer part of their body. Forensic science has told us when they do an autopsy on the dead body they find soft tissue, for example the heart, the liver, the brain, etc. has been destroyed to a greater or lesser degree. Of course we do not see this when looking at the dead body, only when we go into the body parts.

These newtons in time which have energies flow through the soft tissue in a similar direction, that is a straight line until they are restrained by a combination of the skeleton and the skin of the deceased. The newtons travel, for example, starting from the centre of your brain and making a beeline to your skull destroying any brain tissue in their path. Subsequently, energising your skin then dissipated going back to the big bang.

I use other examples of this. All over the world you will see and can buy second hand Kevlar motorcycle helmets in perfect condition. These often have come from dead motorcyclists. The Kevlar helmet can sustain many more newtons without being destroyed than the brain can accommodate.

In all this the lesson must be not to energise objects beyond their ability to dissipate newtons in impact time and this goes irrespective of the object, for example, earthquakes and skyscrapers.

Other examples I use to explain this phenomenon is the concept of explosive decompression. This concept is known to all engineers working with high pressure fluids. I will explain it by reference to what happens to an apparently solid elastomar (hydrocarbon compounds that elastically deform at ambient temperatures and are to varying degrees porous) when subjected to high pressure gas environment.

The high pressure gas, driven by many newtons and containing many newtons, permeates into the elastomer. As the pressure increases it will take the path of least resistance which in all probability will not be a straight line. If you release the pressure instantaneously the newtons within the gas that has permeated the elastomer will go back to form and try to follow a straight line. By this travel path and the increase in gas particle size, the elastomer can be completely destroyed.

There are of course instances of this happening with the bodies of deep sea divers hence one of the reasons for slow decompressions for sub-sea divers.

I also refer to experiences as a chef cooking kippers: an inexperienced chef will on a barbecue burst the kipper by applying too many newtons too quickly in the form of heat over a small time period which energises the fluid within the kippers, tuning it into a gas which will attempt to escape as a newton in a straight line bursting the kipper.

In a similar manner, this cook will also burst potatoes by boiling them too quickly at too high a heat.

It's a Newton

We now go on to an experienced cook barbecuing sausages (Pølse – a Norwegian sausage). The first action is by using a fork to break the skin in a few places. This permits the newton to escape if done correctly. The skin of the sausage doesn't burst.

Unfortunately we cannot prod motorcar passengers in a similar manner but if you have a nose bleed following an accident, you dissipated the newtons over too short a time period.

There are many different forms of energy. However, when you look into them all they have a common currency which is newtons and time and this currency exists in a place we call space.

**CHAPTER 6**

# Pressure

Derived concepts such as pressure are far easier to understand. The difficult part is now over without using formulas.

Once you have the concept of what a newton is, what you add to newtons to get pressure is simply divide the newtons by the area they are acting on. The newtons effectively spread over that area and you will get the pressure acting on the area.

Needless to say, if there are no newtons, there is no pressure. Needless to say, if the newtons act on a small area, i.e. an infinitively small area, the pressure will be infinite. Similarly, if the same newtons acts on a very large area (an infinite area), the pressure will be infinitely small.

In my lectures I try to describe this as follows.

*Figure 6*

*Figure 7*

It's a Newton

I am in the middle of a boxing ring, in one corner there is a small girl with a stiletto heel in her hand (figure 6), in the other corner there is the heavy weight boxing champion of the world with boxing gloves on (figure 7). I must fight one. They are both going to hit me in the head, one with a boxing glove and one with a stiletto heel. To which one do I run to be assaulted? It is not the little lady.

On a safety issue, we do a lot of pressure testing in our company and I am always concerned, if part of a pressure retention envelope (a boundary similar to a skin that retains a volume of fluid and this skin (envelope) ensures that fluid does not come into contact with an adjoining volume of lower or higher pressure), say a screwed plug, ruptures under pressure. The newtons that have produced the pressure give energy to that plug. Interestingly, the preferred direction of the energised plug is a straight line if there are no other external forces applied to the plug. There can be instances where such a plug will behave in a similar manner to

Pressure

that experienced by a bullet emerging from a rifle.

**Needless to say, you should never stand in the line of a force, a newton or still worse, a pack of them.** Explosions produce many newtons dependant on the fuel. It is remarkable how we can view material in the area behind the big bang horizon. In that, prior to the initial explosion and the realisation of these newtons, time, space and matter in some form existed.

In our business as engineers we also are concerned with implosions. These normally occur where we have made a vacuum in the pressure retention envelope or a different pressure exists at each side of the envelope.

We are all familiar with our school day prank of creating a partial vacuum in a plastic drink bottle, i.e. the walls of the bottle implode, a force (newtons) caused this acting on the area of the outer skin of the bottle. These newtons are transported through the air we

NOTES

breathe. They exist, these newtons, all around us packed in our atmosphere. This atmospheric pressure is a result of a column of individual gas particles existing in every part of the earth, growing less dense as we leave the earth's surface. All the particles being attracted to the centre of the earth by a concept called gravity.

This can lead to some very interesting engineering opportunities on the bottom of the ocean, down holes on the deepest oil wells and up in the place we call space (subjects for another book).

In the next chapter I am going to speak of stress and its Siamese twin strain.

## CHAPTER 7

# Stress and Strain

What do we add to newtons to get stress?

We divide newtons by area again.

Stress has a remarkable similarity to pressure and has the same units, no newtons = no stress.

What is strain?

Strain is induced by stress. If there is no stress, there are no newtons and there is no strain. If there are newtons there will be stress and therefore there will be strain.

Depending on the materials, the relationship of stress to strain is constant within the elastic limit of the materials and identical materials behave identically.

This relationship of stress and strain I describe as I described the newton, I use the human body (see figure 8).

In figure 8 you try to pull one hand from the other, you experience tensile stress and tensile strain in your arm.

NOTES

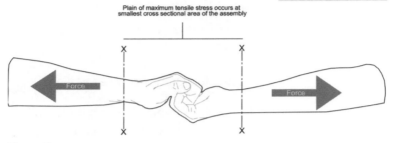

Plain of maximum tensile stress occurs at smallest cross sectional area of the assembly

Force

Force

*Figure 8*

In figure 9 you try to push one hand against the other, you experience compressive stress and compressive strain in both arms.

NOTES

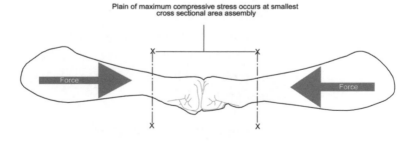

Plain of maximum compressive stress occurs at smallest cross sectional area assembly

Force

Force

*Figure 9*

It's a Newton

In figure 10 you try to move the palm of one hand against the palm of the other hand. In this instance your arms and your hands experience shear stress and shear strain.

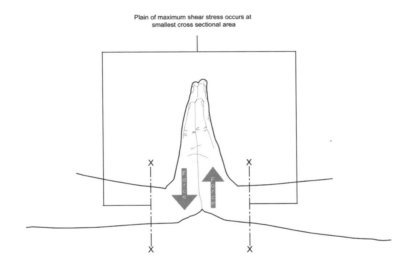

*Figure 10*

Stress and Strain

In figure 11 you are using the fist acting on the palm of one hand and you are experiencing in your elbow on one arm and the shoulder joint on the other torsional stress and torsional strain.

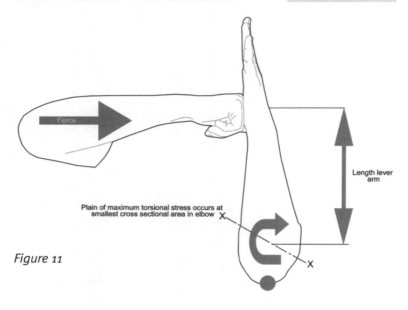

Figure 11

Of course if you were to supply sufficient newtons to go above the elastic limit of your body parts, you would eventually pull your muscles and break your bones.

In the lectures I show some engineering structure and ask the apprentices what

It's a Newton

forms of stress and strain are acting on the members of the structure. Often, in fact normally, we get combinations of stresses and strains and show how they are added and indeed subtracted on occasions.

Heat and temperature gradients bring with it their own form of stress and strain as does friction conditions. Indeed, there are many many types of stresses and strains. However, they all start and begin with the newton and end with the newton.

I have now finished my little book.

Thank you for reading it. The next one will not be so long in coming.

**CHAPTER 8**

# Epilogue

So now we all have it.

The same understanding of newton, time, space, matter, energy, pressure and stress that I give to the apprentice group without using any formulas, relying only on the three of the five available human senses. Those being touch, sight and hearing.

Not only no formulas but no definitions either.

My old professor in Strathclyde was correct. Why have I not used the two remaining senses of smell and taste? I must be missing something.

I am going to think more on this as I study the other dimensions beyond the big bang horizon.

There is no doubt in my mind that Messer's Newton, Rankine, Kelvin, Maxwell, Einstein and others share my view. It is just a great pity that some of us, can not equate the formulas produced by these gentlemen to obtain a clearer understanding and vision of the newton, time, space, matter, energy, pressure and stress.

According to Newton, forces are equal to something – a formula. According to Einstein, energy, similarly is equal to something – a formula. On reading this book the reader should appreciate that whilst the newton may be equal to something, it exists in its own right. This must be so, because we feel it.

Once you read this book you will notice that all formulas in the public domain can be written solely using these concepts. My principle conclusion to the reader is; transport any formulas that give you a problem into their fundamental building blocks and all the formulas will then make sense. The vision is the horse; the formula is the cart.

Thanking God as I do for the vision.

It's a Newton